Because I/we care:

Presented to

____

____

From

____

____

Date

____

Special thanks to
Debbie Loveall and Anna Jackson
for their invaluable assistance

LIFE'S EMERGENCY HANDBOOK

KIRK CAMERON
RAY COMFORT

Bridge-Logos *Publishers*
Gainesville, Florida 32614 USA

Life's Emergency Handbook
Bridge-Logos Publishers
P.O. Box 141630
Gainesville, FL 32614, USA
www.bridgelogos.com

ISBN 0-88270-921-6

Edited by Anna Jackson and Lynn Copeland

Research by Anna Jackson and Debbie Loveall

Design and production by Genesis Group

Cartoons by Richard Gunther

Cover by Andy Toman

Printed in the United States of America

CONTENTS

(in alphabetical order)

PREFACE

Life has many emergencies. Most take us by surprise. Others come a little slower. Take for instance when it rains here in Southern California. The first thing we do is explain to alarmed young children why the sky is leaking.

Precipitation in the area is so rare that people don't know how to drive on a wet road, so we then turn on the TV to see how many accidents have occurred. There are usually around 800 in the two-hour morning commute. Tragically, some even lose their lives, simply because they don't slow down in the wet conditions on slick, oily roads.

Many of life's emergencies are avoidable, such as accidents at intersection lights. Few people bother to glance in both directions before taking off when the light turns green. All it takes is a faulty light, a car being chased by the law, or someone speeding through a red light, and suddenly they become another statistic. We live in a world that begs for tragedy. Roads were originally designed for horse-drawn carriages. Rarely was there a head-on collision (there was plenty of "horse sense"). Then came the automobile. At 15 mph most

head-on collisions were avoidable, but as speed increased, authorities did something wonderful to protect drivers. They painted a line down the middle of the road to keep oncoming cars apart. How thoughtful. Bear in mind that if the driver on the other side of the line is insane, drugged, tired of living, drunk, on the phone, rubber-necking, picking up his cigarette lighter off the car floor, or is as absent-minded or as sleepy as you are, your life is in mortal danger. So if you have a two-lane road, it makes sense to drive on the lane furthest away from the center, if you have a choice. Slow down in the rain, don't tailgate, look ahead of the vehicle in front of you, stay clear of trucks on the freeway—these things are common sense. Oh, and remember: statistics reveal that every fifteenth car has a driver who has been consuming alcohol. So count the cars and stay clear of the fifteenth vehicle.

You will notice that cartoons throughout this book provide a touch of humor. We asked our good friend Richard Gunther to do this simply because humor can help us remember important information. We are more likely to recall a picture of someone touching a live wire and having his hair stand on end than a generic illustration. The humor is in no way meant to demean the seriousness of the issues addressed. We have also included silly little poems with certain emergencies (the type where one's mind tends to go blank). We can often recall poems word for word many years after we learn them, so if such an emergency does arrive, hopefully the poem will remind you of the procedure you should follow.

We have drawn from many experts when compiling this book. Most gave wonderful advice, while others made us question their expertise. Take for instance the "expert" who suggests that if you are ever in an alley and someone pulls a gun on you, the best way to get the attention of passersby is to yell, "Fire!" It seems that people tend to immediately respond to a fire. Correct us if we are wrong, but is it sensible to call "Fire!" to someone who is pointing a gun at you?

Most people don't know what to do when confronted by an emergency. It is so easy to forget what we have learned. For example, we asked several people what they should do if their car slips off the road into water. Some said they remembered that there was a procedure, but they weren't sure what it was. They thought that perhaps it was to wait in the car until it settles on the bottom. In case you don't know, that's not the right thing to do, especially if your car slips into the Pacific Ocean.

It is our hope that you find the information in this small book helpful, perhaps even life-saving.

KIRK CAMERON
RAY COMFORT

Special Note: While this book was in production, my sister-in-law and her five kids came to visit. As we were watching the children, we looked across the room at her one-year-old son who was lying in front of a fireplace. He had been leaning his hand and face against the glass door of the fireplace, although he wasn't screaming. When she picked him up, we saw that his flesh had burned to white. We called 911 and the hospital for instructions, but they refused to give advice over the phone. I remembered that I had *Life's Emergency Handbook* on my laptop and pulled up "Burns." Within seconds, I could tell my sister-in-law what to do.

I'm so glad I had the information on hand. I actually used this book before it was even printed! My nephew was taken to the hospital with second-degree burns, but soon recovered.

— Kirk Cameron

Because of this incident, we created a website to provide free access to the information in this book: *www.emergencyhandbook.com*

Disclaimer:
Every effort has been made to provide accurate information. However, the authors and publisher assume no legal liability for the accuracy, completeness, or usefulness of any information disclosed herein.

EARTHQUAKE

1. When the shaking begins

If you're indoors, take immediate cover in an interior doorway or under a heavy table (make sure that it is strong). Protect your eyes by pressing your face against your arm. Keep away from bookshelves, china cabinets, and windows—anything that could topple over on you, or glass that could shatter and cut you. Don't go outdoors. People are often hurt by falling debris when exiting a building during a quake.

If you're outdoors when the earthquake strikes, get into an open area as quickly as you can. Drop to the ground so that you won't be knocked off your feet and injured. Remember that bricks and other items can dislodge from buildings and fall on you, and telephone poles can topple, so an open area is safer.

If you're in a vehicle during an earthquake, slow down and drive away from bridges, overpasses, and electrical wires. Then stop your car and stay inside the vehicle. When the shaking ceases, proceed with caution, watching for roadway, bridge, and overpass damage.

2. Aftershocks

Be ready for aftershocks to occur minutes, hours, or days later. These are often responsible for bringing down additional buildings that were damaged during the initial earthquake. This is why it is important to stay out of any damaged structures until officials report that it's safe to go back inside.

3. When the shaking ends

If you smell any gas, immediately open a window and leave the building. Shut off the outside main valve if you know where it is. Then call the gas company.

Inspect your home for broken wires or sparks. If you see damage to your wiring, immediately shut off the electricity at the main circuit breaker or fuse box. Do not do this if you have to step into water to do so; instead, call an electrician or the power company.

In area-wide emergencies such as an earthquake, it's wisest *not* to immediately call family and friends to check on their well-being or to report on your own. Instead, leave the phone circuits open for emergency calls.

4. Preparation

You can greatly minimize danger by bracing everything in your home. Brace bookshelves to the walls and light fixtures to the ceiling. Use metal straps to brace your water heater to wall studs. It is wise to have your cabinet doors fitted with latches, and keep heavy items on bottom shelves.

Keep an emergency kit centrally located in the home. You should have at least three gallons of water per person, a change of clothes and a sturdy pair of shoes for each person, canned food and a can opener, a first-aid kit, small quantities of essential prescription medicines, a flashlight (with extra batteries), cash, and a battery-powered radio so you can stay informed.

MEMORY HELP

Be prepared, that's what they say
It could come any time—night or day
Store first aid, water, and shoes
Flashlight and food, and you'll never lose
After the ground shakes for what seems like an hour
Check the gas, then turn off the power.

BURGLARY

1. During a burglary

If you find your house is being broken into while you are at home, call the police immediately. Never try to confront a thief. Many thieves carry guns and they are ready to kill if necessary. If you wake up and find a burglar in your room, pretend to be asleep. Again, avoid any confrontation. If the thief is not in your room, loudly yell, "Jeff, get the gun while I call the police!"—whether or not there is a "Jeff" or a gun. This may have the effect of causing the criminal to panic and run out of your house.

2. After a burglary

If you find your house has been burglarized, leave it immediately—you don't want to take a chance on running into the thieves, who may still be inside. Go to a neighbor's house and call the police from there. When the police arrive, take notes as you speak with them, making sure you take down the case number. Also make sure that you take photographs of the burglary scene before you begin to clean things up.

If credit cards, checks, or ATM cards were among the stolen items, be sure you cancel them immediately. This is why it is wise to make a photocopy of all your important cards and file them in a safe place.

Make lists, as detailed as you can, of everything that was stolen. Contact your insurance company and give them a copy of the list, as well as the case number the police gave you. They may also want a copy of the pictures you took. In the days and weeks that follow, you will almost certainly discover other items that are missing. To double check that you haven't simply misplaced them since the burglary, look carefully over the photos you took on the day of the theft. If you don't see the missing items in those pictures, there's a good chance they were indeed stolen. Contact your insurance company about these additional items as soon as possible.

Also, find out how the thieves entered your home, then do whatever is necessary to prevent anyone from getting in again. If there is no sign of forced entry, have the locks changed immediately.

3. Preventive Measures

Remove any shrubs near doorways and windows, to eliminate places where a thief could hide while breaking into your house. Consider installing an alarm system.

Make sure the outside of your home has good lighting at night. Install photoelectric cells on your outside lights so lights will automatically turn on at dusk and turn off at dawn.

Leave some lights on throughout your home all night. If you are leaving on vacation, plug a couple of lights, and perhaps a radio, into small electrical timers. Set the lights to turn off and on in your typical pattern so it will appear that you are at home.

Ask a relative, friend, or trusted neighbor to pick up your mail and newspaper daily, to avoid notifying others that you are out of town.

If you have a cell phone, keep it in the bedroom with you at night. That way if a thief removes the phone from the hook, you can still call for help. If you live in a high-risk area, you may want to install a bolt on your bedroom door and use it at night.

Take a detailed inventory of your household items—including photographs, model and serial numbers, and appraisals of expensive items—and keep it in a safe place such as a safe-deposit box. That will make it much easier to identify items that have been stolen when filing police reports and insurance claims.

One former burglar said that his best advice on how to avoid being robbed would be to get two dogs, and make sure they bark.

MEMORY HELP

It's night—you hear a creep in your house
Pick up the phone, as quiet as a mouse
Call the police, then hang up the phone
Don't let the burglar think you're alone
"Jeff, call the police; I'll get the gun!"
When the creep hears that, he's sure to run.

HURRICANE

1. Basics

A hurricane is a storm with sustained winds greater than 74 mph. Hurricanes are the most costly of all natural disasters. Back in 1992, Hurricane Andrew caused nearly thirty billion dollars worth of damage. They have also been the most costly in terms of human life. In 1900, a hurricane in Galveston, Texas, took an incredible 6,000 lives. No other natural disaster in U.S. history comes close to that number of casualties.

More people are killed by what's called "storm surge" than by the hurricane itself. The storm surge is a huge wall of seawater caused by the hurricane as it moves onto the shore. It can be up to 20 feet high and 100 miles wide. Homes and businesses near the beach are often destroyed by this tsunami-like wave. Nine out of every ten deaths associated with hurricanes are due to storm surge. This is why you must pay attention not only to hurricane watches, but also to coastal flood watches as well.

2. Stay informed

During hurricane season, stay informed about the weather by radio or television. Hurricane season in the U.S. runs from June through November, with August and September being the peak months.

During times of impending storms, be constantly aware of weather conditions, because advisories can be updated to more severe categories at any time.

A "hurricane watch" means that a hurricane is *possible* within 36 hours; a "hurricane warning" means that the storm is *expected* within 24 hours.

A "coastal flood watch" means that the *possibility* of seawater flooding exists on coastal areas within the next 12 to 36 hours. A "coastal flood warning" means that flooding is *expected, has already occurred, or is in the process of occurring.*

3. Advance Preparation

If you live in a coastal area, it's wise to be ready. At least two hurricanes strike the U.S. each year.

Have an evacuation plan. Depending on the hurricane severity, you will probably need to go at least 30 to 50 miles inland. With the increased traffic that accompanies an evacuation, it will likely take three times longer than normal to reach your destination.

To protect your home, create "storm shutters" by cutting pieces of half-inch marine plywood to fit each window. Pre-drill holes around the edges at approximately 18-inch intervals. Write on each shutter the window it fits. When a hurricane approaches, simply use a screw gun to put your storm shutters up.

Trim dead and weak limbs from trees regularly. Cut down trees that might pose a risk during a hurricane.

Stock up on batteries whenever you find them on sale. Extra batteries will keep you informed of weather reports.

Consider obtaining flood insurance, as homeowner's policies don't cover damages from the flooding that accompanies hurricanes.

Assemble a standard emergency kit. This should contain at least three gallons of water per person, a change of clothes and a sturdy pair of shoes for each person, canned food and a can opener, a first-aid kit, essential prescription medicines, a flashlight, extra batteries, cash, and a battery-powered radio. As you prepare for a hurricane, you may also want to include pillows and blankets, important financial paperwork, and your camera for taking pictures after the storm for insurance purposes.

4. As the storm nears

During the hurricane watch, listen to the radio for reports. Put up your storm shutters and remove any objects from your yard such as children's toys, garden tools, and lawn furniture. Make sure you fill your car with gas, and review your evacuation plan with your family. Turn your refrigerator and freezer to their coldest settings; this may help minimize any food spoilage while the power is out. Fill every available container with clean drinking water—including cleaned sinks and bathtubs.

5. When the storm strikes

When a hurricane warning is issued, if you're in a mobile home, evacuate immediately. Otherwise, you may choose to stay in your home if no evacuation order has been given. If you do stay, go to the first floor to a room located near the center of the dwelling. Stay away from windows. Use battery-powered lights, not candles. Once the storm strikes, travel is very dangerous, so do not leave your home unless instructed to do so by officials. If the power goes out, unplug all your major appliances; this will reduce any damage caused by a power surge when the electricity comes back on.

If an evacuation is ordered, unplug appliances, turn off the electricity, and turn off the water at the main valve. Grab your emergency supplies, wear protective clothing, and leave as soon as possible.

6. Don't be fooled by the "eye" of the storm

The eye, or center, of the hurricane is a deceptive calm, so don't be fooled into thinking that the storm has passed. If you are in the eye you *do not* have time to travel anywhere in safety. Therefore stay in your shelter until you get an official word over the radio that the storm has completely passed. Tornadoes are often spawned at the edges of the hurricane's eye.

7. After the storm

Don't return home until officials instruct you that it is safe to do so. Bridges may have been washed out. *Never* drive through floodwaters across roads—your car can be swept away in a moment by a very small amount of water. Never drive around barricades—there could be electrical lines down and you could be electrocuted. Be cautious when entering your home. Snakes or other animals may have entered your home seeking shelter. Remember to take pictures of all damage for the insurance company. If necessary, open doors and windows to let air circulate to help dry out the dwelling.

DROWNING

1. Basics

When someone has inhaled water, you must get emergency workers to the victim as quickly as possible. Professional emergency care is a *necessity*. Even a tiny amount of water left in the lungs can be fatal.

Be aware that diving accidents often produce neck and spinal injuries, so try to support the victim's back and neck, keeping them rigid and moving them together. If neck or back injuries seem to be present, avoid moving the person—wait for emergency workers to arrive. They have the equipment and experience necessary to move the victim safely. Statistics show that over 30% of all drowning victims have elevated blood alcohol levels.

2. Reaching the victim before he drowns

If the victim is alert and within reach, try to pull him to safety by extending a pole, oar, rope, or stick. If he is too far out, throw a life ring attached to a rope and pull him in. If no life ring is available, throw the victim anything that will float: a life vest, cooler, surfboard, beach ball, or capped milk jugs. This will help the victim keep his head above water while you find a way to throw him a rope and pull him ashore.

Unless you are a trained lifeguard, you could lose your life by trying to rescue a drowning victim. Drowning victims can become hysterical and grasp for anything to stay afloat. They can easily pull a rescuer under the water and drown him. Therefore, follow the procedure lifeguards use: approach the drowning person from behind, talking calmly to him as you do so. Tell him to extend his arms out in front (away from you). Then grab a piece of clothing, or cup one hand under the victim's chin and pull the person back.

3. Perform the Heimlich maneuver

If the victim is conscious but is choking on water, perform the Heimlich maneuver as you would on any other choking victim. Stand behind him and wrap your arms around his waist. Then make one of your hands into a fist and place the thumb side of that fist against his upper abdomen. This should be above the navel, just below the rib cage. Grasp the fist with your other hand and press into his upper abdomen with a quick upward thrust. Do not squeeze the ribcage, but confine the force of the thrust to your hands. Repeat until water no longer flows from his mouth.

If the victim is unconscious, place him on his back. Turn his face to the side to allow water to drain from his mouth. Kneel down with one leg on each side of his hips. With your hands on top of one another, place the heel of your bottom hand on his upper abdomen below his rib cage and above his navel. Lean your body weight into quick upward thrusts into his upper abdomen. Repeat this process until water no longer flows from the mouth.

According to a 1986 study published in the *Journal of the American Medical Association*, a drowning victim who is given CPR alone has only a 50% chance of surviving—but if the airway is emptied of water by using the Heimlich maneuver before CPR begins, his chances of survival jump to an incredible 97%.

4. Begin CPR if necessary

Sometimes the Heimlich maneuver alone is enough to "jump start" the breathing and heartbeat. If the victim is not breathing, then begin rescue breathing immediately. Check for a pulse. If there is no pulse, begin CPR immediately. You should take a class on CPR in case of an emergency. If you have not had a class, and you are in an emergency situation, there is a chapter in this book on CPR. (See page 70.)

5. When the victim revives

If possible, remove any wet clothes and wrap the person in warm, dry towels or blankets. Keep him comfortably warm, still and calm. *Do not* let the victim walk around. Instead, lay him on his back and prop his feet up about 12 inches. This will help minimize shock. Keep a close watch on his breathing and pulse, as you await the arrival of emergency workers.

FLOOD

1. Basics

While floods can sometimes develop quickly during times of prolonged rain or winter ice melt, they generally take several days to reach their peak.

Flash floods are usually the result of an extremely heavy rainfall or a dam bursting, and often occur without any warning. A flash flood can create a wall of water 10 to 20 feet high that will demolish buildings, bridges, and anything else in its path. Your only chance for survival is to get to higher ground *fast*. These floodwaters may carry debris such as building materials, trees, even cars and trucks.

2. When flooding is possible

Listen to a battery-powered radio and follow the instructions from officials. Keep your family ready to evacuate. If you live in a low-lying area, an evacuation order might not come until *after* the roads around your house are already flooded, so keep an eye on the roads and make sure you leave in time. If you live in an area that is

flood-prone, try to keep your vehicle well-fueled during the rainy season.

Even if the flood never approaches your house, there may be a disruption in your fresh water supply after a flood. Scrub out your bathtubs and sinks with bleach and fill them with clean drinking water. Also fill all available jugs, bottles, pots, and pans. The general rule is a gallon per person, per day.

Bring in everything from your yard that you don't want floating away—all yard furniture, children's toys, etc. Move any valuables to the upper floors in your house.

3. Avoid walking through water

If you're caught outdoors during a flood, never walk through water down a street—you may step into an open manhole or be sucked down a sewer drain. Don't underestimate the power of flowing water. Trying to walk through just six-inch-deep, fast-flowing water can knock you off your feet and sweep you away. In addition, downed power lines can shock you from 100 yards

away with the electrical current traveling through water on the ground. Stay on dry ground, or move to higher ground and stay there.

4. If caught in a flood, get out of the car

Think you can drive your vehicle through floodwaters? It takes only two feet of water to cause a *bus* to float downstream! Lighter cars and trucks can be swept away and rolled over in seemingly shallow water. Your car will *not* protect you; you can be trapped in it and drown.

If you approach a flooded area, turn around and go a different way. If your vehicle stalls, get out and leave it. Your life is more important than a vehicle. If floodwaters begin to surround it, abandon it. Eighty percent of the people who die in floods drown inside their vehicles. Many of those deaths occur because people try to save their cars.

5. After a flood

When officials announce that it is safe to return to your home, be cautious as you drive. The flood may have washed out roads and bridges, so listen to the radio for announcements about which roads are safe to travel.

Do not enter any building that is still partially submerged in floodwaters. If the building has been flooded, walk around the outside and look for cracks in the foundation. Be sure to look at the walls, windows, and doorways. If there is any sign that the building is in danger of collapsing, do not enter for any reason.

Be on the lookout for any animals, especially poisonous snakes, that may have entered your home with the flood debris. Wear durable shoes, and be cautious of damp ceilings that may fall. If you have flood insurance, take pictures for insurance claims.

Never turn on any appliances that were submerged in water during the flood, including your heater and air conditioner. They could short out and become a fire hazard. They must be inspected and reconditioned by a professional before they can be used safely.

Floodwater often contains raw sewage, gasoline, oil, and chemical byproducts, so be sure to wash your hands with soap and clean water anytime you have come into contact with floodwater or objects that have been exposed to the flood.

As you begin the clean-up, first clean walls and floors with soap and water, until all the mud is gone. Next, wipe down all surfaces and mop the floors with a solution of 1 cup of bleach to 1 gallon of water. When pumping water out of a flooded basement, do so slowly —only one-third of the water per day—to avoid structural damage due to stress.

Throw away all food that has come into contact with floodwater. Canned goods that have not been damaged may be used after the entire can has been disinfected with bleach.

If you have a public water supply, officials will announce when it is safe to drink it again. If you have a water well that has been flooded, it will need to be disinfected and tested before it is safe to drink from again. Drink only bottled water until your water source is approved for use. If you have no source for bottled water, pour a gallon of water through a coffee filter, boil it for at least three minutes, then add ¼ teaspoon of bleach. Let it sit for one hour before drinking it.

6. Preparation

If you live in a flood-prone area, have "check" valves installed on all your sewer piping to keep floodwater from backing up through the pipes into your home.

Take a detailed inventory of your household items—including photographs, model and serial numbers, and appraisals of expensive items—and keep it in a safe place such as a safe-deposit box. If your home does flood, and you have flood insurance, this information may help when you file your insurance claim.

Keep an emergency kit handy. You should have at least three gallons of water per person, a change of clothes and a sturdy pair of shoes for each person, canned food and a can opener, a first-aid kit, essential prescription medicines, a flashlight, extra batteries, cash, and a battery-powered radio.

KILLER BEES

1. Basics

Africanized Honey Bees are nicknamed "killer bees" because of their aggressive nature, which is so different from the common European Honey Bee. Killer bees are more easily disturbed, attack in greater numbers, chase their target over greater distances, and sting more frequently than their European cousins.

2. Beware of nesting areas

Killer bees nest in places you might not expect to find bees. These include garbage cans, soda cans, old tires, attics, empty flower pots, abandoned vehicles, holes in cacti, walls, porches, utility boxes, and underground mouse nests. If killer bees are known to be in your area, eliminate as many nesting areas as possible around your property—but do so very *carefully.* Get rid of all trash. Stuff wall cracks with steel wool and seal with caulking.

3. Avoid being attacked

The bees are easily provoked into attacking by vibrations

or even by loud noises. They are attracted to dark clothing and hair. As much as possible, stay away from potential nesting areas, and remain alert outdoors. If you see bees going in and out of any area, or if you hear the hum of an active bee colony, *move away quickly.* Don't even give the bees the chance to chase you. Run before they know you are there. Call your county's Animal Control office and report the swarm.

4. If you are attacked

Run away! Run as far and as fast as you can from the hive area. Africanized bees will pursue you for up to 150 yards—that's 1.5 football fields in length. They fly approximately 15 mph. Try to run through tall brush and weeds to confuse the swarm. If you dive into water, swim underwater as far as you can from the entry point before you come up for air.

Find shelter as soon as possible. If you stand still and swat bees, you will almost certainly be stung to death. Every time you kill a bee, the scent released agitates the bees further. Given the opportunity, Africanized bees will not stop stinging you until you are dead. You must run. If you cannot run because of disability or poor health, try to cover yourself in leaves or dirt as a last resort.

The bees will target your head, so put anything available over your head to protect yourself. If you have nothing else, pull your shirt over your head, or cover your eyes, nose, and mouth with your hands.

5. After you get away

If you get stung, use the edge of a credit card or a knife to scrape stingers out of your skin. Never try to remove them with by pinching or tweezing, as this will squeeze more bee venom into your skin. Get the stingers out as fast as possible, because they may continue to pump venom into your skin for up to ten minutes.

If you're allergic to bee stings, you need to immediately inject yourself with epinephrine from a "bee sting kit" prescribed by your doctor. Then quickly get to a hospital emergency room. Even if you don't think you're allergic, seek emergency help immediately if you've been stung more than twelve times, or begin to develop swelling of the tongue or throat, difficulty breathing, racing heartbeat, or loss of consciousness. Don't forget to call your county's animal control office to report the swarm.

HEART ATTACK

1. Basics

A heart attack occurs when the blood supply is cut off from part of the heart muscle, causing that part of the heart to die. The attack interrupts the heart's ability to work properly, and can lead to death. Surprisingly, 15% of all heart attacks are completely painless. The damage from these *silent* heart attacks is often discovered accidentally during medical tests for something unrelated.

These silent attacks weaken the heart muscle, and may explain why 25% of the people who die from a heart attack have had no previous history of heart-related problems. These people often delay getting emergency help because they assume their pain couldn't possibly be a heart attack. However, even athletic young people die each year from sudden, unanticipated heart attacks. Anyone experiencing the symptoms of a heart attack should seek emergency help *immediately*—regardless of their previous health history, level of physical fitness, age, or gender.

2. Symptoms

Heart attack pain is usually intense. The victim will probably be short of breath. He may begin to sweat, or become nauseated and dizzy. The pain in the center of the chest often radiates down the underside of his arms, the left arm particularly, sometimes all the way to the fingertips. Often, pain is also felt in the jaw. There is a sensation that the chest is being crushed or squeezed. Sometimes the sense of being crushed is even more intense than the heart pain.

3. CPR

Try to keep the victim as still and as calm as possible, while awaiting the arrival of emergency workers. Be prepared to perform CPR until the emergency workers arrive. Forty percent of all heart attack victims die before they reach the hospital, because in most cases no one was available to perform CPR in those first vital moments. You should take a class on CPR to be ready for such situations. There is a chapter on CPR in this book. (See page 70.)

4. Angina

Some of these same symptoms can occur in a common condition known as *angina*. Angina is caused by insufficient blood flow to the heart. Angina pain seldom lasts longer than three to five minutes and is almost never accompanied by sweating, nausea, and dizziness. Whenever you experience chest pain, seek medical help to determine the cause.

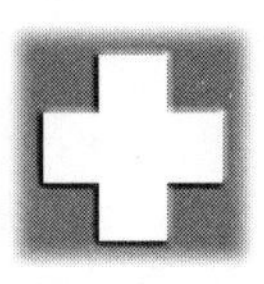

PANIC ATTACK

1. Basics

A panic attack happens when the body and mind suddenly manufacture all the characteristics experienced during a time of extreme terror—even though there is no real danger. Studies have shown there may be a hereditary (biological) component to the attacks. They usually occur for the first time in early adulthood following a stressful life event such as the birth of a child, the death of a family member, or a graduation.

2. Symptoms

The person experiences a feeling of paralyzing terror—but the fear has little or nothing to do with the circumstances surrounding him. The body releases adrenaline which causes a "fight or flight" response. He feels as though he is going crazy, or is about to die. As his heart races and he has difficulty breathing, he may also experience dizziness, nausea, shaking, or chest pains. These attacks occur without warning, and can even happen while the person is asleep.

3. Remain calm

Even though the person is terrified, a panic attack is not physically dangerous, and will usually pass within a few minutes. However, since repeated panic attacks may occur for hours, stay by the victim during the attack, and attempt to reassure him that he is not going crazy. If you remain calm, you will help him to calm down. If possible, have him go to an unoccupied room. Away from the stares of strangers, he will have fewer distractions while waiting for his fear to abate and his body to return to normal.

4. Calming the mind

Panic attacks begin in the mind, but they trigger very real physical symptoms in the body. So the key is to calm the mind. If you have a panic attack, breathe as deeply as you can, and then exhale through your mouth (not your nose) extremely slowly. This may make you feel slightly faint (if so, wait for a moment, then try again). Do this five times, blowing the air out through the mouth as though you are silently whistling. This simple solution helps for two reasons.

First, it will provide oxygen for the brain. A panic attack makes the heart race, raising the body temperature and causing sweat to appear on the skin. The extra heart activity therefore needs an influx of oxygen. If the heart began racing (and raised the body temperature) because you were running, the lungs would automatically pull in the necessary oxygen (even when you stop running, the body continues to pull in oxygen by panting). But because you are stationary, there is no deep breathing and thus the brain is deprived of sufficient oxygen. The symptoms of a thumping heart, sweat (which is the body's reaction to keep itself cool), and the lack of oxygen to the brain (which deprives it of the ability to think coherently) cause more panic. This is why you may feel as though you are losing your mind and that you have no control over the situation. It is therefore essential to get oxygen back into the brain so that the mind, instead of going blank, can begin coherent thought and bring calm back to the body. Deep breathing does this.

The second benefit of deep breathing is to give the mind something to do. If you occupy it with concentrated thought (and if you understand what you are trying to do), you will crowd out thoughts of panic.

5. Another key

Another great key to conquering panic attacks is to become philosophical about them. They can build character in your life by making you empathetic to the suffering of others. They will also make you thankful for things in life that you normally take for granted. You can either consider the attacks as stepping stones in life that you are going to keep beneath your feet, or great rocks that are going to fall on you and crush you. The choice is yours. A positive, thankful, empathetic attitude will begin a path of healing.

Keep yourself from falling into a pit of self-pity by realizing that any suffering you are going through with these attacks is relative. Whenever you feel sorry for yourself and are tempted to drown your sorrows in alcohol, think of a person who has suffered burns over 70% of his body—including the face. That will bring your suffering into perspective.

One great concern of panic attack victims is the fear of having an attack in public. This fear of a public attack can even set one off if you are suddenly confronted in public by someone you know. It may therefore help if you carry an interesting book or pictures of your children, or something that can become an easy talking piece. That will get the attention off you, onto the book, pictures, etc. Knowing that you have a way of "escape" will bring you comfort, and help you begin the path of healing.

HEAD INJURY

1. Basics

Head injuries are among the most deadly of accidents, because the brain may be injured. Even a superficial scratch to the head can cause serious bleeding. A blow to the head, even if it leaves no marks, can cause the brain to bump the inside of the skull, resulting in a concussion.

2. Minor scratches and bumps

If the injury appears to be a minor scratch, treat it as you would a similar injury to any other part of the body. Minor scratches and scrapes to the head usually bleed much more profusely than similar cuts anywhere else. The amount of blood lost can be frightening, but simply apply direct pressure to stop the bleeding. When the bleeding ceases, use ice to help relieve pain and swelling. If the bleeding doesn't stop after fifteen minutes of direct, continuous pressure, seek medical help, as the injury may be more extensive than you first assumed.

If it appears to be a minor bump, and the person is

not showing any unusual symptoms, use ice on the bump site to help relieve pain and reduce swelling. Check on the person every two hours for the next twenty-four hours. Set a timer and wake him up every two hours during the night. If there are any unusual symptoms, or if you can't get him to wake up—get emergency help immediately as the injury is probably more serious than you thought.

3. Major head injuries

If you know the blow to the head has been severe, seek emergency help immediately. Unless you absolutely know otherwise, assume the victim has neck and spinal injuries too. Do not move him unless his life is in immediate danger.

If you did not see the injury happen, and you can't discern whether or not it was caused by a significant blow to the head, get professional help immediately. Major head trauma may leave only a scratch or a small bump.

If the person starts exhibiting any of these symptoms, get emergency help immediately: vomiting, convulsions, vision trouble, paralysis, loss of consciousness, pupils of unequal sizes, a deep cut on the skull or face, a deformity (dent or large swelling) of the skull or face, a bruise or swelling behind the ear, black eyes, or one eye that appears to be sunken. The victim may complain of pain, ranging from a mild headache to severe pain. Watch for personality changes. If he becomes irritable, angry, unreasonable, or shouts inappropriate words, this is a major sign that a life-threatening head injury has occurred.

If the victim is conscious, talk to him. Ask questions that will make him concentrate. Sometimes just keeping the victim alert until emergency workers arrive can be the difference between recovery and coma.

4. Control bleeding

Do not wash, wipe, or try to clear debris or hair out of the wound. If there is a skull fracture, this could drive debris or skull fragments further into the brain. Try to control bleeding, but *never* apply direct pressure to any part of the skull if there is a dent, if you see bone fragments, or if you see that the brain is exposed. Don't try to stop any blood or fluids that flow from the nose or ears. The fluid is one sign that the skull has been fractured, and it must be allowed to drain. Trying to stop it could increase pressure on the brain and further aggravate the injury.

If the skull appears intact, apply direct pressure to stop the bleeding. Use a sterile cloth bandage on the wound, then place your hand on top of that. Once the bandage becomes blood-soaked, don't remove it—add new bandages on top of it.

SEIZURE

1. Basics

A seizure is a misfiring of electrical impulses in the brain. A convulsive seizure causes sudden uncontrollable muscle contractions (convulsions). Many conditions can bring about a seizure, such as a head injury, a reaction to drugs or alcohol, or even an infection. A high fever can cause *febrile* seizures that are sometimes associated with mumps, measles, or spinal meningitis in children. Diabetic insulin shock can bring on a seizure, and cerebral palsy sufferers sometimes experience them. Having seizures repeatedly is known as *epilepsy*.

2. *Never* put anything in the person's mouth

It is a myth that people having seizures will "swallow their tongue" or "bite their tongue off." Some old first-aid manuals suggest prying open the seizure victim's mouth and inserting something, like a "bite stick" or a wallet. This is now known to do nothing but cause teeth and jaw damage to the victim. It can even present a choking hazard if part of the material breaks off in the victim's mouth. *Never* try to insert anything into the mouth of a seizure victim. Most sufferers never bite their tongues, and even if they do, it is usually not serious and will heal quickly.

3. Partial seizure

A partial seizure affects only part of the brain, and usually begins with the victim appearing dazed. He may be staring and blinking, there may be jerking movements in a certain part of his body, or he may be performing repetitive acts such as opening and closing his mouth. The victim will often walk around, and may repeat a phrase over and over again.

If a person is having a partial seizure, carefully move sharp objects out of his way. Do not try to physically restrain him—allow him to walk if he is doing so. When he comes out of the seizure, speak softly and reassure him as he becomes reoriented. A partial seizure can sometimes lead to a generalized seizure; if this happens, don't be alarmed. Remain calm.

4. Generalized seizure

A generalized seizure affects the entire brain. The most common generalized seizure is the *grand mal*, in which the person loses consciousness and falls down. The body becomes rigid, the person may lose control of his bladder and bowels, and may even stop breathing momentarily. Intense muscle contractions cause the body to jerk violently and the victim may drool. This usually lasts only one or two minutes; if it lasts longer than five minutes, call for emergency help immediately.

If a person has a generalized seizure, carefully move sharp objects out of his way. Do not try to physically restrain him. The involuntary muscle contractions are so strong that you could cause great injury to yourself and/or the victim by trying to hold him down. Put something soft under his head, or sit on the floor at his head and gently try to keep his head from striking the ground. Roll him onto his side so that saliva can drain out of his mouth and not cause a choking hazard. Some people remain unconscious for hours. As he regains consciousness, gently reassure him as he becomes reoriented.

5. When to call for emergency help

Call for emergency medical help any time a generalized seizure lasts longer than five minutes or if someone has two seizures in a row without fully recovering from the first one. If there is paralysis after the seizure, seek emergency medical help. Also call for help if the person has never had seizures before, or there is reason to suspect the seizure was caused by anything other than epilepsy.

FIRE

1. Basics

Each year, 4,000 people die in house fires in the U.S. Most house and apartment fires start in the kitchen, usually the result of unattended cooking or human error. Most deaths due to fires are caused by careless smoking habits. Children and senior adults are the most frequent victims, because they are unable to escape quickly.

2. Three minutes

If you are in a building that's on fire, don't stop to call 911 or to rescue any property. Get out immediately! If you awake to a fire, you may have as little as three minutes to escape. Remember that it may have taken a minute for smoke to activate your alarm and another minute for you to be awakened, leaving you only one minute to escape from the flames. Speed is absolutely essential.

3. Crawl out

Fire can fill your home with thick, black smoke in a matter of minutes, so it may seem as if you are suddenly

blinded. Because you won't be able to see, you can easily become disoriented in a home you've lived in for years.

If the room is filled with smoke, immediately drop to the floor and quickly crawl out. The only breathable air will be near the floor—but even that won't last for long. Modern construction materials and furnishings release odorless, colorless toxins as they burn. Inhaling these fumes may quickly cause you to become drowsy and disoriented. Resist the urge to inhale until you get near the floor. The majority of fire casualties are caused by breathing smoke and deadly gases.

The fire will also superheat the air. Within five minutes the air can be 100 degrees at floor level, and easily 600 degrees at eye level—much hotter than an oven. Inhaling it would sear the inside of your lungs.

4. Doors offer some protection

Never open a door that's hot! If your smoke alarm sounds, even if the door feels cool to the touch, brace one shoulder against it and open it slowly. If hot air and smoke come in, slam it shut and take another escape route. Since doors can provide such vital protection, you should never sleep with bedroom doors open. With open doors, your life could be taken by toxic fumes even before your smoke detector goes off.

5. Stay out

Never go back into a burning building. Call 911 from a neighbor's house, and await the arrival of firefighters. Although pets are often considered beloved members of the family, do not reenter the building to attempt to rescue a pet and risk your own life in the process.

6. After the fire

After the fire department tells you it's safe to enter the building, try to locate important documents such as your driver's license, social security cards, credit cards, and medical information. You may need to board up windows and doors to discourage looters. Do not consume any food or medicine that has been exposed to heat, soot, or water. Notify your insurance company of the fire.

If the structure is uninhabitable, you'll need to contact several other agencies to let them know what has happened: your mortgage company, your child's school, your employer, and your post office. Also call police to let them know the property will be vacant for a time.

Contact the Red Cross if you need medicine, clothes, or a place to stay; they will be able to help you, or can point you to agencies in your community that can help. Save all your receipts for things you have to purchase after the fire. These expenses may be important for insurance claims, and for your taxes the following year.

7. Preventive Measures

Smoke detectors should be installed on every floor of your home. Place them near likely fire sources, such as in the kitchen and laundry room, as well as within 15 feet of each bedroom. Change the batteries twice a year, using the start and end of daylight savings time as a reminder.

A five-pound fire extinguisher costs less than having a pizza delivered, so the next time you are in a discount store, buy one for your kitchen. It will be money well spent. Not only might it save your property, but also the life of someone you love. Use a fire extinguisher only on small, contained fires; if the fire has begun to spread, close the door to the room and get out of the building immediately.

Have a primary and an alternate escape plan. Decide on a prearranged meeting place outside your home to ensure all family members have escaped safely. Once a year, practice escaping from your home by crawling on your stomach with your eyes closed. A good escape plan gets everyone out of the house in only thirty seconds. Practice is *especially* important if you have small children.

Have a thorough inventory of your possessions, with

photographs and copies of important documents, stored in a safe place such as a safe-deposit box. This information may help when you file your insurance claim.

8. Special notes for multi-story buildings

When you hear the building's fire alarm go off, feel the door. If the door is cool, brace your shoulder against it and open it slowly. If there is no smoke in the hallway or stairwell, follow your building's emergency evacuation plan. If you encounter smoke or flames on the way down, return to your apartment. If there is smoke in the hallway, or if hot air and smoke come in when you open the door, slam your door shut.

If the door is warm, call 911 and tell the emergency workers exactly where you are. It's important that they know each room that is occupied—so don't assume that someone else calling 911 is enough. Use a wet towel or blanket to stuff under the crack in the door. Cover air vents to keep the smoke out. If possible, open your windows at the top and the bottom. Don't break the windows; you might need to close them later if smoke starts to come in from outside. Hang a bed sheet out of the window to help firefighters locate you. It may take some time before they can get to you, so don't panic.

9. Special notes for college campuses

The misuse of cooking appliances in dorm rooms, combined with the overtaxing of outlets with power strips and extension cords, greatly increases the risk of fire. Among fire-related deaths on college campuses, alcohol consumption is the most common contributing factor.

A dangerous "herd mentality" effect occurs when students hear a fire alarm and look around to see that no one else is reacting to it. Because they see that no one else is evacuating, they also ignore the alarm. Make sure you are not part of this deadly mistake. One or two people evacuating at the sound of the alarm can motivate the herd and save countless lives. So, even if you know it's a false alarm, you should get out of the building anyway! Make false alarms into a contest if that helps—any time a fire alarm goes off, the last one out of the building buys the pizza.

MEMORY HELP

Room fills with smoke, house is on fire
So remember the saying, "It's hotter when higher"
If you want to keep breathing, drop to the floor
Then, crawling along, head for the door
You're not going to open it, just feel if it's hot
If it's cold, open slowly; if it's hot, *do not!*

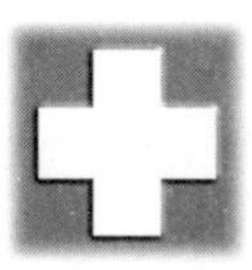

HEAT STROKE, EXHAUSTION, AND CRAMPS

1. Heat stroke

Heat stroke, also called "sun stroke," is a medical emergency that can lead to death. It can come on suddenly, and need not be preceded by heat exhaustion or heat cramps. With heat stroke, the body loses its ability to cool itself. Most heat stroke occurs on hot, humid days, but can also occur on hot, dry days. Symptoms of heat stroke are: hot, dry skin (little or no sweating); alternating deep breaths followed by shallow rapid breathing; throbbing headache; dizziness; nausea; and confusion. Heat stroke victims often lose consciousness, and may even slip into a coma. Call emergency help immediately.

It is vital to get the victim's body temperature lowered quickly or brain cells will begin to die. Rapidly cool the person with whatever means are available. For example, put the person in a tub of cool water (constantly watch him to prevent drowning), spray him with a garden hose, or pour the water from a cooler onto him. If possible, get him indoors to an air-conditioned room. If ice is available, pack some under each armpit, under both knees, on both sides of the neck, and in the groin area. If no water or ice is available, quickly get the victim into shade; remove enough clothing to cool him and fan him vigorously with some of the clothing, as you await the arrival of emergency workers. If the victim begins to twitch or convulse, try to prevent him from harming himself, but *never* put anything into the person's mouth.

2. Heat exhaustion

A person with high blood pressure or a history of heart trouble should seek emergency medical help at the first sign of heat exhaustion. Most cases occur during summer heat waves. The symptoms of heat exhaustion are: cold, clammy skin; excessive sweating; rapid, shallow breathing; total body weakness; nausea; and dizziness that may lead to fainting. If the person faints and does not recover quickly, call for immediate emergency help.

Get the victim to a cool place to rest. Remove enough clothing to cool him. Spray him with water and fan him;

or put him in a tub of cool water (constantly watch him to prevent drowning). Have him drink cool liquids. Sports drinks are best, if available. Otherwise, mix two tablespoons of sugar and a sprinkle of salt in a glass of water. *Never* give alcoholic beverages, as they cause dehydration. Also, never give liquids to an unconscious person. If the symptoms aren't gone within an hour, or if they worsen, call for immediate emergency help.

3. Heat cramps

Someone on a low-sodium diet or with a history of heart trouble should see a doctor for heat cramps. The air need not be excessively hot for heat cramps to occur. Heat cramps can easily happen when someone has been working hard and is sweating profusely. The symptoms are muscle cramps (usually in the abdomen, legs, or arms), weakness, and heavy perspiration.

At the onset of symptoms, the victim should stop all activity and rest in a cool place. Massage the cramping muscle and apply warm, moist towels to the cramp area to minimize discomfort. Have the person drink cool liquids. If sports drinks are not available, mix two tablespoons of sugar and a sprinkle of salt in a glass of water. *Never* give alcoholic beverages, as they cause dehydration. The victim must not return to strenuous activity for several hours; to do so could lead to heat exhaustion and even heat stroke.

CHOKING

1. Basics

If someone is unable to speak and is clutching at their neck, this is the sign that he is choking. The victim may even start to "turn blue," as his oxygen supply is cut off.

2. Never slap the back

Old first-aid manuals recommended slapping the victim on the back between the shoulder blades. However, this actually has the effect of further lodging the object in the airway—so *don't* do it.

3. Perform the Heimlich maneuver

For an infant, lie him down on his back. Take the index and second fingers of both of your hands and place them on his upper abdomen below the rib cage and above his navel. Press into the abdomen with a quick upward thrust. Be very gentle. Repeat until the object is expelled.

For children and adults, stand behind the victim and wrap your arms around his waist. Make one of your hands into a fist and place the thumb side of that fist against his upper abdomen, between the navel and the rib cage. Grasp the fist with your other hand and press into his upper abdomen with a quick upward thrust. Do not squeeze the ribcage, but confine the force of the thrust to your hands. Repeat until the object is expelled.

If the victim is unconscious, or you cannot get your hands around his waist, lie him on his back. Kneel with one leg on each side of his hips. With your hands on top of one another, place the heel of your bottom hand on his upper abdomen below his rib cage and above his navel. Lean your body weight into quick upward thrusts into his upper abdomen. Repeat until the object is expelled.

If you are choking and no one is around to help you, place your fist with the thumb side on your upper abdomen, between your navel and rib cage. Grasp the fist with your other hand and use quick upward thrusts to try to expel the object. If that does not work, lean over an object like the edge of a table or the back of a chair, and try to use it to make the quick upward thrusts needed to expel the object.

4. Begin CPR if necessary

If the victim is not breathing after the object is expelled, then begin rescue breathing. Check for a pulse. If there is no pulse, begin CPR immediately. You should take a class on CPR in case of an emergency. If you have not had a class and you are in an emergency situation, there is a chapter in this book on CPR. (See page 70.)

5. Get the victim to a hospital

Even if the object has been expelled, it could have caused damage to the throat area. If the Heimlich maneuver was performed roughly, there could even be damage to the abdomen. A choking victim should always see a health professional as soon as possible after the incident.

MEMORY HELP

Baby chokes, begins to turn blue!
Don't panic, now what should you do?
On his back is how he should lay
Then two strongest fingers is the right way
To press above his button, under his rib
Repeat until dislodges, onto his bib.

BLEEDING

1. Direct pressure

If a wound is bleeding profusely, seek emergency medical help immediately. Until emergency workers arrive, the best method to control blood loss is with direct pressure. If possible, place a clean piece of material directly onto the bleeding site. If no material is available, then use your hand. Apply direct and firm pressure to the wound. It usually takes 10 to 15 minutes of direct pressure to stop heavy bleeding.

2. Elevation

If direct pressure is not working to control the blood loss, also try elevating the bleeding part of the body above the heart. Gravity may help to slow the flow of blood. Do not use this method if the victim has broken bones, dislocations, or possible spinal injuries.

3. Tourniquets are the very last resort

Do not use a tourniquet unless the blood loss is severe, and direct pressure is not working at all. Despite what you see in the movies, tourniquet use may cause the limb to have to be amputated later. If emergency workers are on their way, try to avoid using a tourniquet. Instead, continue applying direct pressure.

If you have no other choice, tighten the tourniquet only to the point at which the bleeding is controlled. Do not tighten further. Once it is on, leave the tourniquet in place—*do not remove it!* Leave that to the medical personnel *only*.

After you've applied it, use a pen to write "TK" and the time you applied the tourniquet on the victim's forehead (e.g., "TK 11:32"). Notifying the emergency workers and hospital staff of this vital information is the victim's best chance to save the limb. If you don't have a pen, memorize the time you applied the tourniquet, and tell emergency workers as soon as they arrive.

4. Amount of blood loss

Try to estimate how much blood has been lost. Think in terms of the amount of liquid in a canned soft drink. How many canned drinks would be emptied to account for the amount of blood that you see? A canned drink contains close to one pint of liquid. Adults, depending on their size, can lose only three to four pints of blood before death occurs. A child can die from a one-pint loss.

5. Once bleeding is controlled, help minimize shock

Shock, a deadly condition, occurs when so much blood has been lost that there is not enough for proper circulation throughout the body. Shock is very serious because, if it progresses too far, the victim will reach a point at which he *cannot* be saved.

A person going into shock may become unresponsive. The eyes may look dull, while the skin is pale, cool, and clammy. The person is often fearful and restless, and may complain of thirst, weakness, nausea, and dizziness.

If you see these signs, and the victim does not have any broken bones or signs of spinal injury, have him lie on his back. Elevate his feet about 12 inches to help keep the blood pressure up a little. Since the body temperature is dropping, it's important to wrap him in warm, dry blankets—but don't cause him to overheat. Do not provide anything to drink, even though the person may be very thirsty; it would likely cause vomiting. Speak gently and reassuringly to the victim while you await the arrival of emergency workers. If the victim remains calm, quiet, and still, his chances for survival increase greatly.

DEATH OF A LOVED ONE

1. Making contacts

This is an emergency that none of us want to deal with, but one that we will all face in time. If the death is unexpected and happens in your home, call 911. They will notify the correct authorities. If it comes after an illness, call the attending physician. If the death occurs in a hospital, you will be told to contact a funeral home for removal of the body.

Next, contact other family members. With most deaths, it is usually wise for loved ones to give themselves time to deal with emotional issues before moving on to deal with the financial, legal, and tax concerns. However, one issue that should be dealt with within a few days is locating the original will. To do so, contact the executor of the person's estate or his attorney. Also, ask the attorney, or the pastor/priest, if any instructions were given for funeral arrangements.

2. The needs of the family

If no funeral instructions were given, the family must

decide if there will be a burial or cremation. Referrals from friends and neighbors are invaluable. There are also memorial societies and funeral associations that can provide practical information. The staff at most funeral homes are skilled at dealing with the emotional and practical decisions that arise when someone dies. Should there be a service at the funeral home or at a church? Should the casket be present or not? If the casket is at the service, should it be open or not? Don't be embarrassed to ask for written estimates of funeral costs.

Most funeral directors will also send the obituary to the newspapers of your choice. Ask the funeral director for an outline/form to use as a guide when preparing the obituary.

If you are planning a service, schedule the date, time, and location to accommodate the needs of family and close friends. This scheduling should be done as soon as possible to allow them to make travel plans.

The person making the arrangements will need to decide whether flowers should be sent, or whether to request that donations be given to a specific charity. Friends may prefer to send a financial gift to the family to help cover costs, which can be crippling. Flowers are pretty, but a check in the mail a few days after the loss of a loved one certainly can be more uplifting than a massive bill. Don't be embarrassed to tell others about this practical way of showing love and concern.

3. Don't hold back the tears

This is a very stressful time for the immediate family. Thoughtful friends and relatives can help with phone calls, errands, childcare, and meals. Don't hesitate to ask for help. Most people don't arrange funerals often enough to be good at it, so the planning can be overwhelming.

- It is important that you take time to grieve and heal. Do not hold back tears. They are a natural release of pain.
- Use this time to draw closer to family members. Take this opportunity to repair any broken relationships.
- Share your feelings with others, especially those who have been through the experience. Consider joining a support group.
- Make sure you eat properly and get exercise. Physical activity releases stress that may build up during this time.
- Your most difficult time may be about six months after the death, when people think you should be over it.

- Try to do things to help others during this time. This will help keep your mind off yourself.

Common physical reactions to grief are: exhaustion, loss or increase of appetite, insomnia, tightness in chest, shortness of breath, and dizziness. Emotional effects may include: numbness, shock, anxiety, guilt, anger, depression, irritability, inability to concentrate, and withdrawal. These feelings are difficult but normal, so take the time to draw closer to God in prayer. Many people find comfort in reading the Book of Psalms in the Bible. (For further information, see "Facing Death" on page 87.)

HYPOTHERMIA

1. Basics

Hypothermia occurs when the body temperature drops below 95 degrees. It doesn't necessarily have to be extremely cold outside for someone to develop hypothermia. It can happen in temperatures of 45 degrees, or even higher if the weather is wet and windy. For the elderly, hypothermia can be a very serious problem. Elderly people are unable to accurately gauge temperature, and often try to live in rooms that are kept too cold in the winter. Hypothermia, however, can also strike athletic hikers or skiers, who do not realize how low their body temperature has fallen. It will quickly lead to unconsciousness and death, if the heat loss continues.

2. Symptoms

Mild hypothermia is categorized by cold, pale skin, and by shivering that may be so severe that the person can hardly speak. If the internal body temperature continues to drop, shivering is replaced by muscle rigidity, uncoordinated movements, and clouded thinking. The victim can then become either unconscious or unresponsive. At body temperatures below 78 degrees, the brain fails and death will occur shortly.

3. Warm the core

Warming a victim too quickly can cause fatal shock or heart failure, so proceed cautiously. Get the person out of the cold and wind. Remove any wet clothing and wrap the trunk area with warm, dry blankets to prevent any further heat loss. To warm up the victim, apply hot water bottles, heating pads, or your own body heat to the victim's trunk area. Place heating pads in the armpits and groin area—but avoid heating the legs and arms. If the limbs become warm before the trunk area is warmed, fatal shock can occur. Therefore, leave the victim's legs uncovered while you warm the trunk area. If the victim is alert, slowly give him warm liquids as you await the arrival of emergency workers. *Never* give alcoholic beverages—they make the body lose heat faster!

CPR

1. Warning

If CPR is performed improperly, or if it is performed on a person whose heart is still beating, it can cause serious injury. Therefore, make sure the victim is indeed unconscious. Tap him gently and yell, "Are you okay?" You must be absolutely certain that the victim's breathing has stopped, and that there is no heartbeat. To be completely prepared, take a course on CPR.

2. Clear airway

Open the victim's mouth and clear any obstructions with your finger. Kneel next to him and put one hand on his forehead. Use your other hand to tilt his chin back—but be careful not to tilt the head back too far. Listen for breathing. Sometimes just opening the airway can enable the person to breathe again.

3. Rescue breathing

If the victim doesn't begin breathing immediately, begin rescue breathing. Pinch his nostrils closed with your thumb and forefinger. Inhale deeply and then place your mouth over his mouth to make a tight seal. Exhale slowly into the victim's mouth. Take 1.5 to 2 seconds to give each breath. The chest should rise. Turn your head and take a second breath and allow air to come back out of his lungs. Give the second rescue breath, then check for a pulse.

Slide your index and middle fingers into the groove beside the victim's voice box (Adam's apple). Feel for a pulse for five to ten seconds. If there is a pulse, continue rescue breathing until help arrives or the victim begins to breathe on his own. For an adult, give one breath every five seconds.

4. Chest compressions

If there is no pulse, begin chest compressions. Chest compressions done improperly can break the victim's ribs—*so please use care.*

For an adult, feel for the place where the bottom ribs join in the middle. The chest compression spot is two finger widths above that. Place the heel of one hand on this spot and put your other hand on top. Hold your fingers up in the air—don't let them touch the victim's chest, as they may cause rib damage. Lock your elbows and press straight down on the heel of that one hand. The chest should be compressed about 1.5 to 2 inches. On the upstroke, take the pressure off the chest, but make sure the heel of your hand stays in contact with the victim's chest.

One cycle is fifteen compressions and then two full breaths. Repeat this cycle four times, then check the victim for a pulse. If there is still no pulse or breathing, continue chest compressions and rescue breathing until help arrives.

MEMORY HELP

Do CPR if there's no beat of the heart
Clear the airway, and you're ready to start
Tilt the head back, but not too much
Two fingers above the cage is where to touch
Put the heal of the hand on top of the chest
Do fifteen pushes, then take a rest
Put your mouth on his, while pinching the nose
Give two breaths; repeat 'til the ambulance shows.

CAR ACCIDENT IN WATER

1. Open a window

If your car slides off an embankment into water, try to open the door immediately. If you cannot because the water pressure outside is too great, unlatch your seatbelt and open a window. Get water into the car quickly, so the pressure will equalize enough for you to open the door and escape. If this is not done quickly, the car will sink with you inside, possibly coming to rest upside down at the bottom.

If you can't roll down a window, try to break one. Don't try breaking the windshield as it's likely made of laminated glass, which is designed not to break easily. Windows are usually made with tempered glass, designed to break into small pieces with rounded edges. Use a small hammer, a tire iron, flashlight, or the metal buckle of your seat belt. Hit the glass repeatedly with sharp blows. If nothing is available, try to break the window with your shoulder. Or, brace your back against the side of the passenger seat and try to kick the window out. If you still cannot open a window, don't panic. The car will soon fill with enough water so you can open a door.

2. Open a door as the water pours in

Hold open the door handle and lean against the door as the water pours in. When enough water is inside the car, the pressure will equalize and the car door will swing slowly open. The car may now begin to sink very rapidly. If you get caught in the doorway and are pulled under, remain calm. Put your foot against the vehicle and push off horizontally away from the car so that you won't be caught in the suction caused by its rapid descent.

MEMORY HELP

Trapped in a car sinking in water
Door doesn't open as you know that it oughta.
Open the window; know what for?
To let in the water to open the door!
Put a foot on the car, then push away
And swim with your might
Toward the light of the day.

DOWNED ELECTRICAL LINE

1. Every wire a live wire

Always assume that a downed electrical wire is energized. The fact that a wire is not arcing (issuing sparks) does not indicate that it is safe to touch or be near. Power could be returned to a downed line at any moment, with no warning. Most electric companies are on a system that will automatically attempt to restore power two to three times each minute.

Even if you know it is *not* an electrical wire, assume it is energized. For example, many people think that the wires that stabilize the utility pole are safe, but this is not the case. A damaged power line could come into contact with that wire at any moment, carrying a deadly charge.

2. Electrocution through the ground

Most people understand that water carries an electrical charge, but did you know that you can be shocked in perfectly *dry* conditions through the ground? This phenomenon is known as "ground gradient," and it's the reason you should always stay as far away as possible from downed lines. The danger zone around an electrical hazard can be as large as 1,500 feet in diameter—the length of five football fields.

If you are walking toward an area where lines may be down, and you begin to feel a tingling sensation in your legs—stop immediately. That sensation is caused by current entering through one of your feet and exiting through the other. You are in danger of electrocution! You cannot simply turn and walk away, because if you step on two sections of ground energized with different voltages, your body will complete the electrical circuit. The only way to avoid risking death is to get one of your feet off the ground. Bend one leg at the knee and grasp your foot with one hand, then hop away from the hazard on the other foot.

3. Saving a life

If you witness a car accident where electrical wires have been damaged, remain at a safe distance, and urge victims to remain inside the vehicle. If they remain inside a grounded vehicle, touching nothing, they are much more likely to survive.

If power lines have come into contact with a person, there is virtually nothing that can be done until they are separated from the current. If you are certain there is no longer any electrical hazard, check the pulse and begin CPR if necessary. Be aware that the body of the victim, though separated from the current, may still contain an electrical charge.

No one should ever attempt to move an electrical wire with a wooden pole, tree limb, or other makeshift device. Trained professionals with specially constructed equipment must do this job. Follow this advice and the life you save may be your own.

ANIMAL BITE

1. Examine the wound

Has the skin been severely mangled? Is the bite on the face? Is there excessive bleeding? In any of these cases, you should seek medical attention immediately. Control bleeding by applying continuous pressure.

2. Wash and wash again

Any animal bite carries with it the risk of infection, especially cat bites. If the wound is not bleeding excessively, your first line of defense is to wash it thoroughly. Use an antibacterial soap to wash the area for 3 to 5 minutes under running water. Rinse the wound completely, then repeat two more times. Dry the wound and bandage it, then see your doctor.

3. Report the bite

Call the Animal Control department in your area and report the bite. If possible, the Animal Control officers will want to capture the animal and observe it for 10 days to be sure it does not have rabies. If it is a pet, they will contact the owner to find out the date of its last rabies vaccination.

4. Rabies vaccination

Any warm-blooded animal can carry rabies, but it occurs primarily in skunks, raccoons, foxes, and bats. Most animal bites are from cats and dogs, but cats are more likely than dogs to be rabid. However, since rabies is fatal, you should see your doctor about a rabies vaccination if you've been bitten and the bite broke the skin.

SNAKE BITE

1. Seek medical attention immediately

Sixteen percent of all snakebites in the U.S. are from poisonous snakes. Never presume that a snake is non-poisonous. Though few people die from snakebites, the danger to your life is very real and should not be treated lightly.

2. Wash and immobilize the wound

Wash the wound with soap and water as soon as possible after the bite. Immobilize the site of the wound by using a splint, if practical. The victim should remain as calm and still as possible. Try to keep the wound level with the heart, or if that's not possible, keep it lower than the heart.

3. Stop venom from spreading

Use two strips of cloth to make constricting bands. These are not tourniquets, and should *never* cut off blood flow; they are to restrict the flow of lymph fluid only. Cutting off the flow of blood will lead to serious tissue damage. They should be snug, but not tied so tightly that you can't slide a finger underneath them. Tie them approximately two inches from the wound, one above it and one below it—but *never* place them on either side of a joint. For example, never place one above and below an elbow. In that case—or any other case where you can only tie one band—opt to place it above the wound (between the bite and the victim's heart).

4. Don't try to suck venom out with your mouth

The poison from *pit vipers* or from neurotoxic (nerve poison) snakes like the *coral snake* can enter your bloodstream through the lining of your mouth. Also, do not cut into the bite area. Many old camping manuals recommended cutting an "X" over the fang puncture marks, but this has been found to do nothing but cause infection problems later.

TORNADO

1. Basics

"Tornado season" runs from March to August, but tornadoes can strike at any time of the year. Most tornadoes occur between 3 p.m. and 9 p.m. Tornadoes typically move from southwest to northeast, but they can change directions at any time. Any time thunderstorms are present, a tornado is a possibility.

2. Be alert—watch and listen

Listen to your local TV or radio station for weather information, and follow their guidelines. A tornado "watch" means that weather conditions make tornadoes a possibility; you should stay near shelter and continue to listen for further updates. A tornado "warning" means that a tornado has been sighted either visually or by radar; take shelter immediately. Keep a battery-powered radio in your shelter so you can listen for further updates.

If you don't have access to a radio or television, be alert to the weather conditions and take shelter at the first sign of a possible tornado. Tornadoes almost always strike at the back side of a thunderstorm. Watch for low-hanging clouds, or for rotation in the clouds. Keep in mind that some tornadoes are almost invisible except for the small cloud of debris they create near the ground. The sound of a tornado has been described as a continuous rumble of thunder, a freight train, or a jet engine.

3. Get out of a car or mobile home

Most deaths during a tornado are caused by flying debris or people remaining inside their cars during the storm. Finding appropriate shelter is your top priority.

If you're caught in a car, get out immediately and take shelter in a strong building. Cars and trucks can be easily tossed around by a tornado (tornadoes have thrown cars up to 100 yards). It used to be recommended that drivers seek shelter under a bridge or overpass, but recent studies have shown this to be very unsafe because of increased wind speed and debris. The air is squeezed as it flows under the overpass, increasing the wind speed. If you cannot get to a building, follow the instructions for taking shelter outdoors.

If you're inside a mobile home, get out! No amount of "strapping" a trailer down will protect it from a tornado. At the first warning of a tornado-producing thunderstorm, you should evacuate the mobile home and take shelter in a strong building. If you have very little warning, follow the instructions for taking shelter outdoors.

4. Take shelter inside a strong building

Once you're inside a strong building, get to the basement or the lowest floor possible. Find a small, windowless room or closet that is located in the center of the building. An interior, windowless bathroom is an especially good shelter because of all the extra framing and plumbing that reinforces the walls. Bathtubs make a good shelter if not surrounded by glass. If an interior room isn't available, take shelter in a room on the north or east side, away from the tornado's typical direction of travel. If possible, get underneath a strong table. If there's no strong furniture to take shelter beneath, then stay next to a wall.

People used to recommend that you open the windows in your home if a tornado was approaching, but experts now know it has no benefit and wastes precious time that should be used to take shelter. Don't go anywhere near windows during a tornado; the high winds and flying debris could shatter them at any moment!

5. Tornado position

To protect your vital organs from flying debris, assume

the "tornado position." Kneel on the floor with your legs tucked underneath you. Lean your upper body forward until your forehead is close to the ground. Clasp your hands behind your neck, and bring your elbows in so that your arms are protecting the sides of your head. Protect yourself from flying debris by covering yourself with blankets, pillows, coats, even a mattress.

6. Taking shelter outdoors if necessary

If you must take shelter outdoors, get to the lowest spot possible, such as an open, low area of ground or a ditch. In this low area, be aware of flooding that may be caused by the storm. Get far away from cars or mobile homes; they may be turned over or tossed in the storm and you don't want to end up underneath them. Lie flat, face-down on the ground with your arms covering your head.

7. Preparation

If you live in an area where tornadoes are a frequent threat, consider having a tornado shelter built. Some pre-fabricated shelters can be easily dropped down into a hole dug in your yard. If a shelter is not possible, consider having a room inside your house converted into a "safe room." A safe room looks like a normal room but has a reinforced ceiling, walls, and door designed to withstand the winds of a tornado. Otherwise, have an area in your home already selected as your tornado shelter so family members will know where to quickly go for safety.

Keep an emergency kit in your shelter for times like this. It should contain at least three gallons of water per person, a change of clothes and a strong pair of shoes for each person, canned food and a can opener, a first-aid kit, essential prescription medicines, a flashlight, extra batteries, cash, and a battery-powered radio.

FACING DEATH

1. The ultimate of life's emergencies

While science and the medical profession can extend our lives, we all still have to eventually face death. Millions therefore take comfort in the Bible, because it claims to have the complete antidote to the "grim reaper." This is its claim: "Christ Jesus . . . has destroyed death and brought life and immortality to light though the gospel." It also tells us that "the gift of God is eternal life in Jesus Christ our Lord."

2. The reason for death

The reason each of us die is that we have sinned against God. The Bible tells us that "the wages of sin is death." We have violated an eternal law. That Law is commonly called "The Ten Commandments." Just as criminals must pay the penalty for their crimes, so we must pay the penalty for our crimes against God. We are in debt to His Law. If we continue to sin, we will pay a terrible penalty.

3. Innocent or guilty?

You may not be aware that you have violated an eternal Law. Let's look at the Ten Commandments to see if you have broken any of them. Have you ever lied (even once)? Have you ever stolen anything (the value is irrelevant)? Jesus said, "Anyone who looks at a woman lustfully has already committed adultery with her in his heart." Have you ever looked with lust? If you have said "yes" to these three questions, by your own admission, you are a lying, thieving, adulterer at heart, and you have to face God on Judgment Day.

Let's look at a few more: Have you put God first in your life and loved Him with all of your heart, mind, soul and strength? Or have you made a god to suit yourself (a god you feel comfortable with)—something the Bible calls "idolatry"? Have you ever used God's holy name as a cuss word? Have you kept the Sabbath holy, honored your parents, or been guilty of greed? Have you ever been angry without cause or hated someone (the Bible says, "Anyone who hates his brother is a murderer")?

No doubt all of us are guilty of breaking some or perhaps all of the Commandments, but we think that God is good, and He will therefore overlook our sins. But it is His goodness that will ensure that murderers, rapists, thieves, liars, adulterers, etc., receive justice. He would be a corrupt Judge if He turned a blind eye to injustice. So listen to your conscience and ask yourself if you will be innocent or guilty on that Day. The fact is we will all be guilty, and if God gives us justice we will receive the punishment that we deserve and end up in a terrible place that the Bible calls Hell. That's not what God wants to happen to us.

4. A complete stranger

Think again of civil law. Imagine if you were found guilty of committing a serious crime. Your problem is that you don't have two cents to rub together. You could tell the judge that you are sorry and that you will try not to break the law again. That won't get you off, because you *should* be sorry, and you shouldn't break the law again. You are deeply in debt to the law and there is nothing you can do about it. Imagine your utter surprise when a complete stranger steps up and pays your fine for you. Suddenly, you are free to leave the courtroom! The law has been completely satisfied through the payment of the stranger.

That's what God did for you. He paid your fine on the cross through Jesus Christ: "God demonstrates his own love for us in this: While we were still sinners, Christ died for us." We broke God's Law (the Ten Commandments), and Jesus completely paid our fine. Then He rose from the dead and defeated death. It's not enough to be sorry or to say to God that you won't sin again. You must repent (turn from sin) and trust in Jesus Christ alone in order to be saved from eternal justice. This is the type of trust you would have when you put your faith in a parachute to save you—it's more than just a "belief."

To receive God's forgiveness and the gift of everlasting life, pray something like this: "Dear God, I know that I have sinned against You. Today I repent of (turn away from) all my sins (name them). I put my trust in Jesus Christ as my Lord and Savior. I thank You that You sent Him to save me from the punishment I deserve. Please forgive me and grant me your gift of everlasting life. I ask this in Jesus' name. Amen." Then read the Bible daily and obey what you read. Look at this incredible promise: "Whoever has my commands and obeys them, he is the one who loves me. He who loves me will be loved by my Father, and I too will love him and show myself to him."

5. The best of all

At the age of thirty-four, a reasonably young Albert Einstein boasted, "I have firmly resolved to bite the dust, when my time comes, with the minimum of medical assistance, and up to then I will sin to my wicked heart's content" *(The Expanded Quotable Einstein,* Princeton

University Press, p. 61). However, time tends to make most thinking men somewhat philosophical. Two months before his death in 1955, he said, "To one bent on age, death will come as a release. I feel this quite strongly now that I have grown old myself and have come to regard death like an old debt, at long last to be discharged. Still, instinctively one does everything possible to postpone the final settlement..." (ibid., p. 63). The great intellectual was right. Death is a debt, and, if we die in our sins, it is one that we will pay for with our very souls. However, it was paid for us in full the moment the Savior cried from the cross, "It is finished." Eternal justice was satisfied, and through Jesus' resurrection death was defeated. If we have repented and placed our faith in Jesus Christ alone, God puts His life in us through the Holy Spirit. The fear of death need never haunt any of us again. We have a glorious future awaiting us beyond death's door. Read your Bible for a preview. A good place to start is 1 Corinthians 15:51–58.

DRUG OVERDOSE

1. If unconscious and unresponsive

If a person is unconscious and unresponsive, check for breathing and pulse. Perform CPR if necessary. Respiratory arrest and cardiac arrest are common in drug overdose cases. Take a CPR training class so you'll be ready. If you are in an emergency situation, and you haven't taken a class, there is a chapter on CPR in this book that will give you the basics. (See page 70.)

Call 911 for emergency help. Tell the emergency worker that you suspect a drug overdose, why you suspect it, and the type of drug used—if you know.

2. If conscious

If the person is conscious but appears to be falling asleep, or complains of sleepiness, engage him in conversation to help him stay awake until emergency workers arrive. Slap his hands or arms lightly to keep him alert. Shout if necessary. Use cold, wet towels on his skin to cause mild discomfort and help him stay awake.

3. Keep yourself safe

If the person has taken certain drugs such as PCP, he may appear calm at first, but become dangerously aggressive. If the person appears dangerous, do not approach him. Do not make sudden movements or turn your back to the person. Back away slowly, while speaking reassuringly. Leave the area and wait in a safe place for emergency workers to arrive. PCP users sometimes kill themselves or others.

4. Don't induce vomiting, unless instructed to do so

Depending on what drugs are involved, and how they were taken, inducing vomiting may not help and may even cause fatal choking. Follow the instructions you are given by the emergency worker when you call 911.

5. Be informed

An overdose does not always mean that illegal drugs are involved. An apparent overdose can simply be an adverse reaction caused by taking two incompatible prescription medications, taking someone else's prescription medicine, or from mixing prescription medications with alcohol or illegal drugs. With every prescription you receive, be sure to ask the doctor about potentially harmful interactions.

BABY DELIVERY

1. Time the contractions

If this is the mother's first pregnancy, her labor will typically last 16 to 18 hours. That time is reduced with each subsequent pregnancy. Contractions usually begin 30 minutes apart and decrease to about 3 minutes apart when delivery is imminent. Based on this information, evaluate whether you can get to a hospital in time. There are many complications that can occur with childbirth, so make every attempt to get to a hospital.

2. Gather a few items and wash your hands

If there is no way to make it to a hospital in time, wash your hands and arms vigorously with antibacterial soap. Also try to compile the following materials:

- A clean sheet or towel in which to wrap the baby
- Heavy twine or new shoelaces to tie the umbilical cord with *(Do not use thread or wire; it might cut through the umbilical cord and the baby could bleed to death.)*

- A towel or plastic bag in which to wrap the placenta

3. Position the mother

Have the mother lie on her back with her knees bent and her feet flat on the floor. If the delivery is taking place in a car, have her lie in the backseat with one foot on the seat and the other on the floor. Place a pillow, or a rolled-up jacket, under the mother's hips, elevating them about 2 inches. This will help her to deliver the baby more easily. Warn the mother that if she feels she needs to vomit, she should turn her head to the side.

4. Help the baby out

When the baby's head begins to show, this is called the crowning. Under no circumstances should the mother be allowed to go to the bathroom at this time, because the birth will likely occur in just a few moments. Most babies are born face-down and then rotate left or right. Spread your fingers out and fully support the baby's head, being careful of soft spots on the baby's skull. If the amniotic sac (the "bag of water" around the baby) has not broken by this time, use your finger to puncture the membrane and then pull it away from the baby's nose and mouth. As the baby moves out, keep its head just lower than the rest of its body to help fluid drain out of its lungs. Do not squeeze or pull on the baby; it will come out on its own. Support the baby throughout the entire process, and be very cautious because newborns are slippery! Once the baby is out, hold it on its side with its head slightly lower than the rest of its body. Wrap the baby in a clean towel or sheet to keep it warm. Tie off the umbilical cord with a piece of twine or shoelace, but do not cut the cord—allow the doctor to do that, so it's done in a completely sterile manner. In most cases, the placenta will be expelled within a few minutes of the baby's delivery. Wrap it in a towel or plastic bag and save it (the doctor will want to examine it). Get the mother and baby to the hospital right away.

5. Emergencies:

Baby's not breathing

Do not slap the baby on its bottom. Make sure mucus is out of the baby's mouth and nose. If the baby's still not breathing, hold the baby on its stomach and gently but vigorously rub its back in a circular motion. If that doesn't help, lightly flick your fingertips on the bottoms of the baby's feet.

Cord is around the baby's neck

As the baby's head comes out, if the umbilical cord is

wrapped around the baby's neck, tell the mother not to push as you gently loosen it. If you can't loosen it, tie the umbilical cord off with the twine in two places about three inches apart, and cut the cord between the tied areas so that the baby can be delivered. You must tie the cord off securely in both places or the baby could bleed to death.

Baby's head does not come out first

If an arm, a foot, or the umbilical cord comes out first, this is a serious medical emergency. Coax the mother onto her hands and knees, then have her put her head down onto the ground. She should remain in this "knee to chest" position while you transport her to the emergency room as quickly as possible. The life of both mother and child are in great danger!

BURNS

1. The degrees

There are three different degrees of burns, in increasing severity.

- *First Degree:* Reddening of the skin; pain; some swelling.
- *Second Degree:* Intense reddening and blistering of the skin; intense pain.
- *Third Degree:* Intense reddening and blistering of the skin, and usually some charred dry black or white areas. Intense pain, or virtually no pain if nerves have been damaged; swelling lasting two days or more.

Immediate emergency help should be obtained for all second- and third-degree burns, and for any first-degree burns covering more than 25% of the body surface.

2. Do not apply ice, ointments, or butter

You should *never* apply ice to *any* burn; the severe change in temperature may cause further tissue damage.

See guidelines below on how to cool different types of burns. Never use creams, ointments, and especially not butter! These things can cause infection. Applying them may even delay emergency treatment because time must be taken to clean them out of the wound.

3. Do not remove "stuck" materials

If necessary, cut around the "stuck" clothing, being careful to leave the pieces that are attached in place. Materials that have become embedded in a burn must be left for the medical personnel to treat.

4. Thermal burns

These are the most common burns; they are caused by fire, hot liquid, steam, or hot objects. Douse the burn with cool water, or cover it with cool wet towels for up to 5 minutes. Wrap the burn in a sterile dry dressing, if available. If the burn is severe, seek emergency care.

5. Electrical burns

These burns are caused by electricity or lighting. If the burn was caused by electricity, first make sure the victim

is disconnected from the source of the current—do not endanger yourself. You cannot receive a shock from a lightning victim.

Electrical burns will usually consist of one wound where the current entered the body and a second wound where it exited. These burns can be cooled using water. While you're waiting for emergency workers to arrive, apply dry sterile bandaging if available.

Be aware that the electrical current often interrupts heart rhythm—be prepared to perform CPR if necessary. Take a CPR training class to be ready for such situations. If you have not taken a class and you are in an emergency situation, there is a chapter on CPR in this book. (See page 70.)

6. Chemical burns

Chemical burns must be treated as quickly as possible; however, you must first make sure the area around the victim is safe to enter. Some chemicals can cause toxic fumes. Protect your skin from contact with any harmful chemicals. If this is not possible, or if the area is unsafe, do not endanger yourself—wait for emergency workers to arrive.

Remove all contaminated clothing and jewelry. If the burn was caused by dry lime, brush it off the person's skin using something dry. When dry lime comes in contact with water it creates a corrosive liquid—so *don't* flush the burn with water *unless* you're sure you've removed all residue *and* you will be able to wash the area with plenty of water, continuously, for at least 20 minutes.

For most other chemical burns, flush the area with flowing water for at least 20 minutes. In most chemical burn situations, it's important to continue the wash for 20 minutes even if the victim reports that the burning sensation has stopped.

7. Molten material burns

If the burn was caused by something such as hot melted plastic, wax, or tar, pour cool water over the burn area until the material cools. Do not try to remove the material. Cover with a dry sterile dressing, if available, and await emergency workers.

CAR ACCIDENT

1. Basics

Vehicle accidents are the number one cause of death for people between four and thirty-three years of age. There are approximately 6 million vehicle accidents in the U.S. each year. In these accidents, 3 million people will be injured, and 40,000 will die. Speeding contributes to about 30% of all fatal crashes, and an alcohol-related fatality occurs every 32 minutes. Car accidents don't just happen to "other people," so be prepared.

2. When no one is injured

If you are in an accident, first check yourself for injuries, then check with the people in the other car. If there are no injuries, follow your auto insurance company's guidelines on how to handle the accident. Most insurance companies urge you to call the police, even if the accident is a minor "fender bender." In some states, the law requires that you call the police even after minor accidents. Find out what the requirements are in your state. In any case, a police report will serve as an objective source of information, in case legal troubles arise later. Make sure you get the police officer's name, badge number, and the number assigned to the report so you can obtain a copy later. Most insurance companies also warn you not to discuss the reason for the accident with anyone in the other vehicle. Don't get into an argument with the other driver, and don't blame or admit fault. To protect yourself, discuss the accident only with the police and your insurance agent.

Write down the make and model of the other car, the license plate number, and the car insurance information for the other driver. Write down the names, addresses, and phone number of everyone in the other vehicle, as well as those of anyone who witnessed the accident. Sketch a little drawing of how the cars are positioned on the road. Note the time of day, the exact location of the accident, and what the driving conditions were like. If possible, take pictures of the accident scene. (You may want to keep a disposable camera in your glove compartment to take pictures of the scene if you're ever in an accident; it may be helpful later in case of legal complications.)

3. When you are injured

If you've been involved in an accident, first assess yourself for injuries. Move your hands back and forth as if you were waving, then try to squeeze your hands into fists. Try the same thing with your feet. Move them back and forth, then try to press down on the floorboards. If you are unable to do those things, assume you have a spinal injury, and remain very still until emergency workers arrive. Tell bystanders not to touch or move you. When emergency workers arrive, tell them you believe you have a spinal injury and why.

If you can move, use the rearview mirror to look at your face. You may not be able to feel pain from your wounds yet, so look all over your body for signs of injury. If you find that you are badly injured, try to remain still and calm until emergency workers arrive. Even though the injury may seem only minor, remain in your vehicle, still and calm until emergency workers arrive. Your injury may be worse than you realize.

If you are bleeding, try to use direct pressure on the wound to slow the bleeding. If you have any large object (such as metal or glass) embedded in your body, *do not* remove it! Stabilize it with your hands, if necessary. Trying to remove it could cause you to bleed to death. One woman survived a horrific accident in which she was impaled through the neck by a fence post, simply because she held the post steady with her hands until emergency workers arrived.

If you have lost blood, you may go into shock—a medical condition that can lead to death if not treated. You may feel weak and dizzy, as if you were going to faint; your breathing may become slow and shallow, and you may feel extremely thirsty or nauseated. If you feel these symptoms and you are able to move, have a bystander help you out of the vehicle. You need to lie down with your feet slightly elevated, and stay comfortably warm until emergency workers arrive. Lying directly on the ground may chill you if temperatures are cool so, if possible, have a bystander place warm, dry blankets under and over you. Even if you are extremely thirsty, *do not* drink anything—it will likely cause vomiting. If you do vomit, have someone help you lie on your side in case you pass out and vomit again while unconscious. Remain as quiet and calm as possible until emergency workers arrive.

4. When someone else is injured

When someone is injured and you call for emergency help, be ready to describe the accident location in detail; look around for the nearest crossroads, mile markers, or highway exits.

Most state laws require that you "render reasonable assistance" to injured people. If you're not medically trained, that may just mean that you try to make the victim comfortable while you await the arrival of emergency workers. If it is a life-or-death situation, some of the chapters in this book may help you keep someone alive until emergency workers arrive. Most states have "good Samaritan" laws to help keep you from being sued for mistakes you might make while trying to "render reasonable assistance." The degree of protection offered by these laws varies from state to state.

5. Someone else's accident—to stop or not to stop

If you witness an accident, you need to stop so that you can give a report to the police. If you are the first on the scene and there are injuries, you need to stop. Turn on your hazard lights (four-way flashers) and, if possible, drive your vehicle at least 50 feet ahead of the accident and pull far off the road. If the accident is completely blocking the road, pull far off the road to the rear of it. Just make sure your car is completely out of the road, otherwise you will cause traffic congestion and may even hinder the arrival of emergency personnel.

If you approach an accident scene and emergency workers (police, ambulance, or firefighters) are already on-site, do *not* stop. Drive cautiously past the accident but don't congest traffic further. Even if there are no emergency workers, but there are quite a few people already helping, do *not* stop unless you have medical training. In that situation you may want to call 911 on your cell phone as you're driving by, just to be sure emergency workers have been notified of the accident.

IDENTITY THEFT

1. Basics

An identity thief steals some vital portion of your personal information and uses it to assume your identity. He can then apply for credit cards, take out auto loans, open cell-phone accounts, forge checks, charge thousands of dollars worth of merchandise, and even file for bankruptcy—all in your name. Identity theft is a federal crime that has been growing by leaps and bounds since the early 1990s.

Identity theft can happen to anyone, anywhere, and may go on without their knowledge for years . . . until the person tries to apply for a loan and is refused because of the "bad credit" caused by the thief. You may be a victim even now.

2. How they do it, and how to stop them

Identity thieves often get the information they need by stealing your mail. If a thief steals one of your outgoing payments on a credit card, they have everything they need to begin their scam. Gone are the days in which

you could put the flag up and safely let the postal worker pick up your mail—today putting that flag up lets thieves know that there is something inside worth stealing. Deposit all your outgoing mail directly into a metal postal box, or do away with your curbside mailbox all together by getting a post office box. Thieves have even been known to submit a change of address form to the post office in your name, diverting your mail to a location where they pick it up.

Identity thieves may also be going through your trash. Don't throw anything away that contains any of your personal information without tearing it into tiny pieces and scattering the pieces between different waste bins in your home. Pre-authorized credit card offers are the worst culprits. You can call 888-5OPT-OUT (567-8688) to make companies stop mailing them to you. While you're still receiving them, make sure you *never* throw them away without thoroughly shredding them. Otherwise, a thief can have the credit card activated by phone, and have the billing address changed so you'll never know what happened.

If your purse or wallet has been stolen, or is missing for a time, you may become a victim of identity theft.

Keep a close reign on your checkbooks, paycheck stubs, and anything else that has your private information on it. Don't share personal information over the Internet by way of email or chat lines—these means of communication are especially vulnerable to computer "hackers."

Your social security number is a primary key in identity theft. Protect your social security number by giving it out as little as possible, and *never* use it as your driver's license number. Also, never print your social security number or driver's license number on your checks.

3. Find out if you've been a victim

The only way to know if you've been victimized is to get a copy of your credit report from the top three credit-reporting agencies: Experian (888-397-3742), Trans Union (800-680-7289), and Equifax (800-525-6285). Request one at least once a year (use your birthday as a reminder). If you've recently been turned down for a loan, or if you have reason to believe you're the victim of identity fraud, you have a right to a free copy of your credit report. If not, you'll have to pay for it. But the cost of all three reports won't be more than a new shirt, and you'll be able to sleep much more soundly at night.

Review your reports carefully for any activity that you have not engaged in. Look for charges to companies you've never done business with, loans you've never taken, and credit card accounts that aren't yours. Also look for "inquiries" that you have not authorized—that means someone is trying to apply for credit in your name. If you find entries like these, you are likely the victim of identity theft.

Even if you're not a victim of identity theft, there's a 70% chance that your credit reports contain some data-entry errors. A data-entry error may say you owe $800 to your credit card company when you owe only $180, or it might indicate you've been late on your mortgage payments when you haven't. Even though these aren't as serious as identity fraud, it pays to get them corrected as soon as possible. You'll have to dispute all the errors, in writing, to each credit agency that lists them. Mail the dispute letters using certified mail, return receipt requested, to prove that each company received your dispute. Keep copies of everything.

4. If you are a victim

First call the fraud departments of all three credit-reporting agencies and request that a "fraud alert" be placed on your accounts so that no new credit will be issued to the thief.

Second, contact every company that provided the thief with goods or services. Ask to speak to someone in each company's fraud department, and explain your situation. Close any accounts that were tampered with by the thief and open different ones with new PIN numbers. Each company will probably require that you send them a completed copy of the FTC's "ID Theft Affidavit" and "Fraudulent Account Statement." Blank forms can be obtained by calling the FTC's Identity Theft Hotline at 1-877-IDTHEFT (438-4338), or by visiting their website (www.consumer.gov/idtheft/). Mail the information using certified mail, return receipt requested, to prove that each company received your information. Keep copies of everything.

Third, file a report with the police regarding the theft. Take down the report number, and make sure you leave with a copy of the report. The companies you're disputing with may also require a notarized copy of the police report regarding the crime.

If you continue to have problems after identity theft, you can request that a new social security number be assigned to you. Call the SSA Fraud Hotline at 800-269-0271, or write to: SSA Fraud Hotline, P.O. Box 17768, Baltimore, MD 21235.